FORK LIFT
TRUCK
SAFETY

Published by Mentor *FLT* Training Ltd.

© 2004 Mentor FLT Training Ltd.
7th Edition 2014

ISBN 0-9549046-0-5

MENTOR

Issued to: _____

Issued by: _____

Date : _____

Contents

Introduction

Fork lift trucks are essential to many businesses and are both efficient and cost-effective. But they can also be lethal weapons that can kill or cause serious injury if not used correctly by trained operators.

As a qualified and trained fork lift truck driver it's **your responsibility** to ensure your own safety – and that of your colleagues and anyone else who may be affected by your actions.

This booklet aims to reinforce your basic training and provide a handy reminder of the key points you need to remember so that you continue to be a safe and effective member of your team.

About this booklet

We've included general information on the safe operation of the most common types of fork lift truck. Please note that your own company's procedures may differ in certain areas such as:

- Use of seat belts
- Battery care and maintenance
- Personal protective equipment

To help you remember the most important points, we've made them stand out like this:

> ## Remember!
> An unladen truck will tip over even more readily than ...

You'll find lots of helpful drawings throughout the booklet to help clarify the main points. These include drawings of several truck types – but don't assume that the words next to these apply only to that truck type unless we specifically state so.

Why we need training

All fork lift truck operators must be properly trained for three main reasons:

1. Safety

This is the most important reason. We want to ensure that:

- Your work place is a safe working environment
- Your business operates safely and efficiently

2. Legal requirements

We must make sure we always meet all the requirements of the law concerning health and safety, and use of equipment.

These include:

- Health and Safety at Work Act 1974 (HASAWA)
- Approved Code of Practice and Guidance (ACOP) L117
- Provision and Use of Work Equipment Regulations 1998 (PUWER)
- Lifting Operations and Lifting Equipment Regulations 1998 (LOLER)
- Management of Health and Safety at Work Regulations 1999

You can find more details of these in the **It's the law!** section of this booklet.

3. Safe practice

Our approved training courses will also:

- Encourage good practice
- Develop safe procedures
- Give you a good working knowledge of the equipment you use

It's the law!

If you drive a car, you have a responsibility to know the traffic laws and Highway Code – and make sure that you follow them. Otherwise you could end up hurting yourself and other people – or worse!

It's the same for what you do at work. As a fork lift truck operator you must know exactly what the law says – and stick to it. In this section, you'll learn about the three main bits of legislation that affect your work:

- ■ Health and Safety at Work Act 1974
- ■ Provision and Use of Work Equipment Regulations 1998
- ■ Lifting Operations and Lifting Equipment Regulations 1998
- ■ Management of Health and Safety at Work Regulations 1999

Health and Safety at Work Act 1974 (HASAWA)

Scope

One of the main aims of this legislation is to involve everyone in the workplace in matters of health and safety: from directors and managers to employees and the self-employed.

The Act also covers members of the public who may be affected by employers' activities.

The employer's responsibilities (Section 2)

The Act says that the employer has a general duty of care to all employees whilst at work, **'so far as is reasonably practicable'.**

Some specific examples of the employer's duties include:

- Providing and maintaining equipment, systems of work and a working environment that are safe and without risks to health
- Making sure there are no risks to health and safety in the use, handling, storage and transport of articles and substances
- Providing adequate information, supervision and training to ensure the health and safety of employees

The employee's responsibilities (Sections 7 and 8)
The Act also states that, as an employee, you have specific duties, which include:

- Taking reasonable care of yourself and other people who may be affected by what you do – or forget to do!

- Co-operating with your employer and other people in all matters of health and safety

- Not interfering with or misusing anything provided in the interests of health, safety and welfare

Remember!

The HSE or local government Environmental Health Office may prosecute you for any breach of these duties in the same way that the police would if you contravened the law when driving a car on the road.

Provision and Use of Work Equipment Regulations 1998 (PUWER)

These regulations apply to the provision and use of all work equipment, e.g:

- Manually operated presses
- Chainsaws
- Milling machines
- Pallet trucks, including manually operated pallet trucks
- Fork lift trucks
- Access platforms and cranes, etc.

More precise information on the above is given in other specialist publications and codes of practice, e.g:

- Rider Operated Lift Trucks Approved Code Of Practice and Guidance
- Lifting Operations and Lifting Equipment Regulations 1998 (LOLER) (see following page)

Regulation 9 of PUWER deals with training requirements, and states that every employer must ensure that:

1. Anyone who uses work equipment has received adequate health and safety training, including training in the methods they may adopt when using the work equipment, any risks involved and precautions to be taken

2. Any of their employees who supervise or manage the use of work equipment have received adequate training as detailed in (1) above

Lifting Operations and Lifting Equipment Regulations 1998 (LOLER)

These regulations deal with the design, inspection, maintenance and safe use of lifting equipment. In general they state that no lifting equipment should be used unless it has:

- Good construction
- Sound materials
- Adequate strength

and is:

- Free from obvious defect
- Properly maintained
- Regularly inspected
- Clearly marked with its safe working load (SWL)

Regular inspections

Any new item of lifting equipment will have been tested and marked with its **SWL** before arriving on site.

Once in service, the equipment must be **thoroughly examined by a competent person** at the following intervals:

- At least every **12 months** if the machine is used only for lifting materials
- At least every **6 months** if it is:
    - used for lifting people
    - an access platform, man-riser type truck or lifting accessory, i.e. a work platform attached to a fork lift truck

Management of Health and Safety at Work Regulations 1999 (MHSWR)

These regulations deal with the management of health and safety in the workplace and place an onus on both employers and employees.

Two regulations that are of particular relevance to the safe use and management of workplace transport are:

Risk assessments (Regulation 3)

- Employer carries out risk assessment for any and all tasks
- From the risk assessment a safe system of work is developed
- The safe system of work must be followed by the employees

Employer's duties (Regulation 14)

- An employee must inform his/her employer if he/she notices anything which could present a risk to the health and safety of himself/herself or others.

Fork lift truck safety

Summary

The four main bits of legislation that affect your work are:

- Health and Safety at Work Act 1974 (HASAWA)
- Provision and Use of Work Equipment Regulations 1998 (PUWER)
- Lifting Operations and Lifting Equipment Regulations 1998 (LOLER)
- Management of Health and Safety at Work Regulations 1999 (MHSWR)

Both employers and employees have responsibilities for taking care of health and safety in the workplace. Proper training of operatives and regular maintenance of equipment are key aspects of these duties.

Remember!

The HSE Enforcement Officers or local government Environmental Health Officers will police all the regulations described in this section.

MENTOR

What's the risk?

Life is full of risks. That's not necessarily a bad thing, but accidents occur when people don't weigh up the risks and take the necessary precautions.

When you hear the words 'risk assessment', what comes to mind? People with clipboards and long forms to fill in?

Actually we all do lots of simple risk assessments every day. Let's take the example of crossing the road. Just think for a minute about:

- How you decide if it's safe to cross the road
- How you developed the judgment and skills to be able to make this decision
- The consequences of letting a child cross the road before they have been trained to do this safely

This section looks at:

- What risk assessment means in the workplace
- Your personal responsibilities for risk assessment
- The causes and results of accidents at work

What is risk assessment?

A risk assessment is nothing more than a careful examination of what, in your work, could cause harm to people. You can then weigh up whether you have taken enough precautions or should do more to prevent harm.

Two key words you need to be clear about are:

- Hazard – means anything that can cause harm (e.g. chemicals, electricity, workplace transport, working on ladders, etc.)
- Risk – is the chance, high or low, that somebody will be harmed by the hazard

Remember!

There are **five steps** you need to follow in any risk assessment:

Step 1. Look for the hazards

Step 2. Decide who might be harmed – and how

Step 3. Evaluate the risks and decide whether the existing precautions are adequate or if more should be done

Step 4. Record your findings

Step 5. Review your assessment and revise if necessary

Personal risk assessment

Although it's the employer's responsibility to carry out a risk assessment and provide a safe system of work for all new tasks, operators should always carry out a personal risk assessment.

You can do this by asking yourself the following questions:

1. What is the task?

Make sure you have thought through exactly what any new task involves before you start.

2. Do I understand how to do the task correctly?

To answer 'Yes' to this question you need to first ask yourself:

- Have I been trained?
- Am I competent?
- Is it a familiar routine task – or a one-off that I'm not sure how to tackle?

If you are sure you're trained and competent – carry on. If not, **stop** and refer to your supervisor.

3. Do I have the right tools and equipment?

Make sure you use the right kit in the right way:

- Is it in good condition or is it damaged?
- Is it up to the job?

If the equipment is OK, then carry on to the next stage. If not, **stop** and refer to your supervisor.

4. Do I know who or what could be harmed?

■ Am I aware of the hazards?

■ Am I aware of other people in the area?

If you aren't aware of what could hurt you or your colleagues, how will you protect yourself and them?

Again, if you can answer 'Yes' to these questions, go to the next stage. If not, **stop** and refer to your supervisor.

5. Are controls in place?

If you know what the hazards are, what controls are there to minimise the risks?

By 'controls' we mean things like:

■ Guards

■ Procedures

■ Personal protective equipment (PPE)

■ Exclusion zones

■ Inspections, etc.

If you do know what the controls are, and they are in place, go ahead with the task **safely**.

If you're not aware of the controls, or they are not in place, **stop** and refer to your supervisor.

You should only carry out the task if you can answer 'Yes' to each of the five main questions on the previous two pages. Anyone who reasonably believes safety could be compromised has a duty to stop the job.

Remember!

1. Examine the task

2. Confirm your competency

3. Check tools and equipment

4. Identify the hazards

5. Implement the controls

Accidents don't just happen!

If you think back to the example of crossing the road, you'll realise there's a link between accidents and risk assessment (or lack of it!).

Causes of accidents

Accidents don't just happen – they are caused by things like:

- Operator error
- Inadequate supervision
- Doing things too fast
- Ground and workplace conditions
- Mechanical state of equipment
- Complacency

The following hazards are common causes of accidents involving fork lift trucks:

General hazards
- Stacked material falling over
- Moving machinery in work areas
- Floor condition and poor housekeeping
- Limited clearance in stacking areas
- Material/debris falling from loads or racking – especially if high
- Obstructions
- Poorly maintained equipment

Environmental hazards
- Background noise from other machinery, vehicles, radios, etc.
- Poor visibility
- Fumes from vehicles/machinery
- No segregation between pedestrians and machinery

Results of accidents

Did you know the HSE estimate that the financial cost of accidents to the UK is currently £14-18 billion per year? And accidents can have a huge personal cost too! They can lead to:

- Personnel injuries – sometimes resulting in death or serious injury/disability
- Social and emotional costs – immeasurable!
- Company costs – damage to equipment, stock, property, etc.
- Legal costs – ever increasing!

Reducing accidents

We can minimise accidents by:

- Complying with the law: HASAWA 1974, PUWER 1998 and LOLER 1998 (see **It's the law!** section of this booklet)
- Training courses to improve skills
- Following safe working procedures
- Safety videos and posters

Personal Protective Equipment (PPE)

Every day we each use some form of personal protective equipment, whether it be the seat belt in your car or an oven glove. There are many types of PPE that will be used in the workplace, the amount of protective equipment that you will require for a task will depend on the level of risk involved. Your employer will have carried out a detailed risk assessment and established a safe system of work to ensure that the correct protective equipment is assigned to each specific task. Before carrying out any task make certain you understand what personal protective equipment is required and how it will protect you. Be particularly careful when carrying out a new task, don't guess what may be required, ask and be sure.

Sections 7b and 8 of the Health and Safety at Work Act 1974 highlight that you as an employee have responsibilities for the use and care of personal protective equipment.

- Section 7b of the act states that you as an employee must cooperate with your employer in matters of Health and Safety, this means that you must wear any PPE provided to you.

■ Section 8 says that you must not misuse or recklessly damage any equipment which is provided for your protection.

Maintaining PPE

If PPE is not properly maintained it will reduce the level of protection it is providing and could result in an accident, regular inspections are essential both before and after use. Make sure that when carrying out maintenance checks you follow the manufacturer's instructions carefully. Should you discover a fault or damage to the PPE report to your supervisor and obtain a replacement.

Remember
Always wear the correct Personal Protective Equipment for the task in hand, it is designed to protect you from possible harm.

Fork lift truck safety

Summary

This section has covered:

- What risk assessment means in the workplace
- Your personal responsibilities for risk assessment
- The causes and results of accidents at work
- Personal Protective Equipment

Remember!

You can help to reduce accidents that could affect you or your colleagues by assessing the risks, looking out for the hazards and implementing the controls.

Understanding the limits

The main point of the last section was that you can reduce accidents by being aware of the risks. However, to make sensible decisions about what you can or cannot do with your fork lift truck, you need to know its limits.

This section will help you understand how the safety limits of your truck depend on its:

- Rated capacity
- Load centre
- Stability

We will explore what affects stability by looking at the principles of counterbalance, and what may cause a truck to become unstable in two directions: lengthwise and sideways.

Rated capacity plate

All fork lift trucks have a rated capacity plate like the one shown below. This contains information on the maximum weight that a machine will safely lift – at a specified load centre and up to a given height.

Note that the lift truck's rated capacity applies when the mast is in the **vertical** position. Special attachments and high lift masts will reduce the rated capacity.

Remember!

It is an offence to exceed the truck's rated capacity or operate a truck not fitted with a rated capacity plate.

Load centre plate

The load centre is the distance from the vertical face of the forks to the centre of the load or the **centre of gravity of the load.**

The diagram below shows a load centre plate:

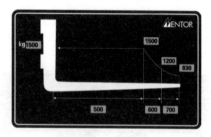

An increase in the load centre distance will decrease the truck's lifting capacity. The plate shown on the previous page shows that the truck could lift:

- A load of 1500kg if the load centre was 500mm from the forks
- A load of 1200kg if the load centre was 600mm from the forks
- A load of 830kg if the load centre was 700mm from the forks

Stability

Fork lift trucks are safe when used by trained operators in the correct way. But problems arise when operators do not follow the rules for safe operation – through either lack of training or a cavalier attitude!

A moving truck is at its most stable when being driven:

- In a straight line
- At a sensible speed
- On even ground
- With the load being carried as low as practically possible – the higher the load, the more unstable the truck becomes
- With the pallet in contact with the fork heels and stabilising back tilt applied – this puts the centre of gravity as far back as possible to aid the stability of the truck and load. It also reduces the overall length of truck and load to aid manoeuvring

Safe travel position
This diagram shows the forks raised enough for load and ground conditions, but kept as low as possible. The pallet is in contact with the fork heels and stabilising back tilt is applied.

Safe park position
This diagram shows the forks as low as possible, with the fork tips resting on the ground. This position ensures minimum risk to people in the area. Don't forget to apply the parking brake and select neutral.

Remember!
When leaving the truck, you should always remove the ignition key to prevent unauthorised use.

Principles of counterbalance

The centre of the front wheel on a fork lift truck is like the balance point on a see-saw – the weight of the load on one side is balanced by the weight of the truck on the other.

Balanced load

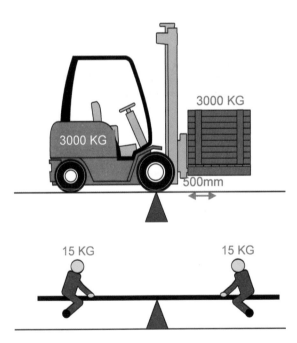

Note the load centre distance on the truck/load shown above.

Heavier load

Now compare it with this load:

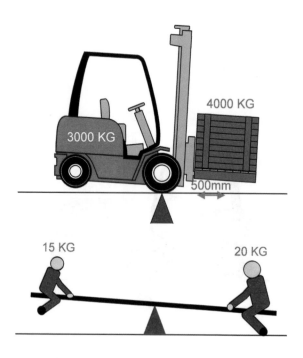

Now the heavier load on the truck is tipping it forwards, just as the larger and heavier child is doing on the see-saw. Note the load centre distance on the truck/load is the same as on the previous diagram.

Increased load centre distance

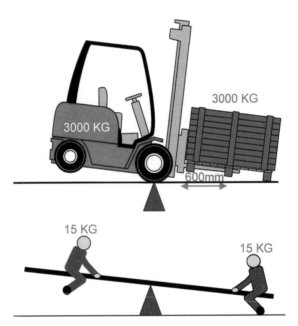

In this diagram, although the weight of the load is the same as the truck, it has tipped the truck forwards. This is because the load centre has increased.

It's the same on the see-saw – although the children are the same weight, the one on the right has moved further out.

Lengthwise instability

The diagrams on the next four pages show eight mistakes that could cause a truck to tip lengthways.

Overloading

The weight of the load on this truck is too great for the rated capacity of the truck, causing it to tip forwards.

Remember!

Exceeding a truck's rated capacity is illegal.

Harsh braking

The driver of this truck has used sudden heavy braking instead of gradual braking. This has caused the centre of gravity to move quickly forwards and the truck has become unstable, shedding its load.

Remember!

Plan ahead – always brake gradually and sympathetically.

Harsh acceleration

This driver is accelerating too fiercely, causing the centre of gravity to move quickly towards the rear of the truck, resulting in the loss of the load.

Remember!

Plan ahead – always accelerate gradually and sympathetically.

Incorrect use of hydraulic controls

Instead of lowering the forks/load gradually, this driver has quickly lowered a heavy load and then equally quickly brought it to a stop. This can result in the increased weight of the load causing the whole truck to tip forwards.

Remember!

Always use all hydraulic controls smoothly.

Incorrect use of tilt

Remember the rated capacity plate and the principles of counterbalance. In normal use, you should only apply enough forward tilt to bring the mast vertical and level the load.

The more forward tilt you apply, and the greater the height, the greater the risk of the truck tipping forwards as the centre of gravity moves ever forwards.

Remember!

Take care when applying forward tilt.

Undercutting

Undercutting means not inserting the forks right up to the fork heels. This increases the load centre and therefore the weight of the load, and badly affects the stability of the truck.

There is also a greater risk of losing the load or tipping the truck over.

Remember!

Always ensure the forks are fully 'heeled'.

Live load

A 'live' load means one that can shift around – this is always awkward to deal with. You need to take great care when accelerating and braking to prevent the load swinging.

If the load swings, the centre of gravity of the truck is moving along with it. This could easily cause the truck to tip over.

Fluid being carried in an individual bulk container will have the same effect as the swinging bag shown in the diagram.

Remember!
Take extra care when handling a live load.

Ground conditions

An uneven surface, e.g. potholes to drop into, or debris to drive over, will cause the truck to lurch and tip – and possibly lose its load or, even worse, tip over.

If you have to drive a truck over a parallel obstruction such as rail tracks or a drainage gully, always drive over diagonally and slowly so **three** wheels are in contact with ground.

Remember!

Always make sure you can see clearly. If your
view is blocked by the load, drive in reverse.

Sideways instability

The next seven diagrams show situations that could
cause a truck to tip over sideways.

Turning at speed

Even with the load being
carried correctly, the truck
will tip over sideways if you
are going too fast and use
the steering incorrectly.

Remember!

An unladen truck will tip over even more readily
than a laden truck. Always drive at a safe speed.

Turning with an elevated load

The higher a load is
carried, the higher the
centre of gravity will be
and the easier the truck
will tip over.

Remember!

Always carry the load as low as possible, and
never turn with an elevated load.

Travelling across a slope

On sloping ground always travel directly up or down the slope – never across it, which would increase the risk of tip over.

Remember!

Never turn on a slope – even with an unladen truck.

Flat or damaged tyre

Driving with a flat (pneumatic) tyre causes the truck to tip towards that side – making it unstable, with the possibility of it tipping over. Chunks missing out of a solid tyre will have the same effect.

Remember!

Never drive a truck with under-inflated or seriously damaged tyres.

Live load

You need to take great care when steering to prevent the load swinging. If the load swings, the centre of gravity of the truck is moving with it. This may well cause the truck to tip over sideways. Fluid being carried in an individual bulk container will have the same effect.

Remember!
Take extra care when handling a live load.

Carrying load off-centre

Carrying a load off-centre causes most of the weight to be carried by one fork. This means that the centre of gravity is all to one side – making the truck unstable.

Remember!
Always make sure you carry the load with an equal weight on each fork.

Ground conditions

On an uneven surface, if one wheel drops into a pothole or drives over debris, the truck will lurch to one side with the possibility of a lost load or, even worse, a tip over.

Remember!

Always make sure you can see clearly and avoid such obstacles. If your view is blocked by the load, drive in reverse.

Summary

You should now understand how the safety limits of your fork lift truck depend on its rated capacity, load centre and stability.

The key points to remember are:

■ You must not exceed the rated capacity or operate a truck which is not fitted with a rated capacity plate

■ An increase in the load centre distance will decrease the truck's lifting capacity

■ A moving truck is at its most stable when being driven in a straight line, at a sensible speed, on even ground, with the load being carried as low as possible. The pallet should be in contact with the fork heels, and stabilising back tilt applied

- The centre of the truck's front wheel is like the balance point on a see-saw
- Lengthwise instability can be caused by:
  - overloading
  - harsh braking or acceleration
  - incorrect use of hydraulic controls or tilt
  - undercutting
  - live loads
  - ground conditions
- Sideways instability can be caused by:
  - turning at speed or with an elevated load
  - travelling across a slope
  - a flat or damaged tyre
  - live loads
  - carrying a load off-centre
  - ground conditions

Maintaining your truck

The last section should have helped you understand what your fork lift truck is capable of – assuming it is in good working order. But a truck will not work well, and may be dangerous, if it's not properly maintained. That's why it's so important for drivers to carry out pre-use checks and report any faults. You also need to understand what the various attachments are for, so that you make appropriate use of them.

In this section we'll cover:

- Pre-use checks
- Reporting faults
- Using seat belts
- Using attachments
- Battery care and charging
- Refuelling

Pre-use checks

We covered the Lifting Operations and Lifting Equipment Regulations 1998 (LOLER) in the first section on page 8.

> # Remember!
> The law (LOLER) requires us to check all lifting equipment.

Pre-use checks are a vital part of fork lift truck operations and must be carried out at the start of each shift or when taking over another truck. You can use the pre-use checklist on the next page for this. You must report any faults found immediately using the forms provided.

The employer and employee both have responsibilities for this:

■ The **employer** must make sure that pre-use checks are carried out, and that records are kept ('safe plant and systems of work')

■ The **employee** must actually carry out pre-use checks before using the truck. Nobody should knowingly operate unsafe machinery

We explain what to check for on each item in the pages following the checklist.

Pre-use checklist

Operator name:	Date:	Time:	
Truck details:			
Item	Not applicable	Check completed	Fault found
Rated capacity plate			
Fork arms			
Carriage plate			
Backrest extension			
Mast			
Mast rollers/slides			
Lift chains and pulleys			
Hydraulics			
Hydraulic controls			
Wheels and tyres			
External condition			
Operating position			
Operator's seat			
Seat belt			
Overhead protection			
Starting procedure (gas trucks)			
Starting procedure (diesel trucks)			
Starting procedure (electric trucks)			
Lights and indicators			
Audible warnings			
Fluid levels			
Drive and braking			
Steering			
Other (specify)			
Faults reported: YES/NO	**Reported to:**		
When:			

What to check

- **Capacity plate** – must be fastened to truck. Check the load/s you wish to lift are within the truck's rated capacity

- **Forks** – check for cracks, fractures, excessive wear, deformity, and ensure they are equally spaced and locking pins engaged

- **Carriage plate** – check for damage or distortion

- **Backrest extension** – if fitted, check for cracks or distortion and ensure it is securely fixed

- **Mast** – check for damage, distortion and cracks

- **Mast rollers and slides** – check the channels and runners for excessive wear or scoring and that there are no objects present which may foul the mechanism

- **Lift chains and pulleys** – check for evidence of deterioration, e.g. loose or worn pins or links. Also check chain anchors are securely fixed. Chain pulleys should be free from damage, uneven wear and flat spots

- **Hydraulics** – check all hydraulic seals and couplings for damage and leaks. Check all hoses for chaffing and that they run clear of obstructions when the mast is operated

- **Hydraulic controls** – ensure smooth operation of all controls to full extent of travel

- **Wheels and tyres** – check wheels for damage and fixing bolt tightness, and tyres for cuts or missing tread causing a flat spot. Also check pneumatic tyres for correct tyre pressure

- **External truck condition** – check overall condition, particularly the condition of the protective covers for engine or batteries. Also check for leaks of fuel, water, hydraulic fluid, lubricants or battery acid

- **Operating position** – check all controls are free from damage and there are no objects present which may foul their use. Check all gauges are operational

- **Operator's seat** – check the anchor points for security and the seat runners and sliders for freedom of movement. Also check for objects under the seat which may foul any safety switches located there

- **Seat belt** – where applicable, check it is in good condition and working correctly

- **Overhead protection** – check it is free from damage and securely fastened to the truck

- **Lights** – where present, check both driving lights and flashing warning beacons are operational

- **Directional indicators** – where fitted, check indicator lights and switch are working

- **Audible warnings** – test the horn and any other audible warning devices (e.g. automatic reversing siren) to make sure they are working well

- **Fluid levels** – check all fluid levels: engine oil, hydraulic oil, brake fluid, water, battery electrolyte, etc, and top up as necessary

- **Drive and braking** – move the truck backwards and forwards and test both the service brakes and the parking brake

- **Steering** – check the steering operation in both directions whilst stationary and on the move. Check for excessive freedom or stiffness of operation

Reporting faults

You must fully understand the fault reporting procedure at your location. This includes how to report faults and to whom, both during the pre-use checks or whilst in operation.

If a truck develops a fault and is being withdrawn from service, make sure you:

- Observe the safe parking rules
- Remove the key
- Place an out-of-use notice in a visible position on the truck

Using seat belts

What does the law require?
In general terms, the Management of Health and Safety at Work Regulations 1999 require employers and the self employed to assess risks and take suitable and sufficient measures to address them.

More specifically, Regulation 27 in the Provision and Use of Work Equipment Regulations 1998 (PUWER) requires the provision of restraining systems to prevent crushing of the operator between truck and ground if there is a foreseeable risk of overturning.

Which trucks are most at risk of overturning?

Centre-control, seated, counterbalanced trucks (which includes pivot steer trucks) below 10,000 kg capacity are at a greater risk of overturning because of the way and conditions in which they are used.

This includes masted and variable-reach trucks such as telehandlers. Side-loaders are also at risk of overturning.

When should an operator restraint be used?

If fitted, you should wear an operator restraint (seat belt) at all times when lift trucks are in motion unless:

- ■ You need to dismount repeatedly and frequently (e.g. to position loads on the forks or check stock levels); and

- ■ The truck is used on a smooth, firm, level surface (e.g. concrete floor); and

- ■ You are unlikely to operate the truck at speeds or in ways which could cause overturning (due to the nature of the operations being carried out and the area in which it is working)

Note: In order to establish the above, a site risk assessment must take place and be properly documented.

Using attachments

Many different types of attachments can be fitted to a fork lift truck – all designed to carry out specific tasks.

Bear in mind that the fitting of an attachment will reduce the lifting capacity of the truck and can also adversely affect stability and manoeuvrability.

Before operating any attachment, you should have received training on its use, including any specific risks associated with it.

When fitting the chosen attachment, make sure it is:

■ Suitable for the truck

■ In good condition

■ Securely attached

On the next few pages we will look at four commonly used attachments:

■ Side shift

■ Reel clamp

■ Fork extensions

■ Working platform fitted to a fork lift truck

We'll briefly describe their main features, what they're for and how to use them safely.

Side shift

What it's for

The side shift is hydraulically operated and can be used for:

- Moving the forks across the carriage
- Repositioning the load during stacking and de-stacking

Safe use

- Always centralise the forks after use
- Make sure you transport loads with the forks centralised

Reel clamp

What it's for

It's hydraulically operated and used for lifting reels and drums etc.

Main features

- The sides of the clamp are shaped to the load
- Some will also have a rotating device to turn the reel/drum through anything up to 360°

Fork extensions

What it's for

Used for lifting and transporting loads which are
larger in size than a normal palletised load.

Safe use

■   Must be inserted at least two thirds of the way
    into the load

■   Will be secured to the truck by pins or chains

Working platform fitted to a fork lift truck

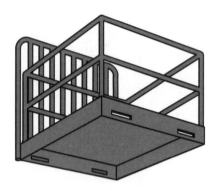

Safe use

- The construction and use of the platform must meet the HSE requirements
- The platform must be firmly secured to the truck
- There must be a safe system of work agreed before the platform is used, i.e. communication between driver and the person on the platform
- The truck driver must remain on the truck at all times when operating with a work platform
- Only authorised persons may be lifted
- The platform, and any truck it is used on, must be thoroughly inspected at least every six months

Battery care and charging

Batteries are the most expensive single item on a fork lift truck, and often the most neglected.

The **main dangers** when charging batteries are:

- Electricity
- Sulphuric acid
- Hydrogen and oxygen (explosive)

Let's look at how to avoid these dangers by using correct procedures.

Electricity

- Use the correct charger for the truck
- Only use insulated tools
- Remove all metal jewellery
- Connect the charger to the truck before switching on electricity supply
- Disconnect electricity supply before disconnecting the charger from the truck
- Isolate all mains supply before starting maintenance
- Ensure there is adequate ventilation.
- A fire extinguisher must be present.
- Personnal protective equipment must be worn at all times.

Sulphuric acid

■ Wear appropriate safety equipment, e.g. rubber gloves, goggles, rubber apron

■ If acid comes into contact with your skin, wash off with plenty of water

■ If acid comes into contact with your clothes, wash off and change the item of clothing

■ If acid comes into contact with your eyes, wash out with plenty of clean water (eye wash) and seek medical attention

■ Do not overfill batteries

■ Clean up any spillage immediately using appropriate materials

Hydrogen and oxygen (very explosive)

- Do not smoke whilst handling or charging the battery

- Expose battery whilst charging to let gases escape

- Remove metal jewellery and use insulated tools

- For topping up use **distilled or de-ionised water only**

- Ensure there is adequate ventilation

- A fire extinguisher must be present

- Personnal protective equipment must be worn at all times

Remember!
No smoking or naked lights in the battery charging area.

Refuelling

It's also vital that you follow correct procedures for refuelling. We'll cover how to do this safely for gas powered trucks and diesel/petrol powered trucks.

Gas powered trucks
To change propane cylinders:

- Park the truck correctly in a designated safe refuelling area

- Close the gas valve and allow the engine to run until it dies

- Turn off the truck's engine and remove the key

- Disconnect the fuel line from the gas bottle

- Release the gas bottle securing strap/s and remove the empty bottle

- Store the empty bottle in its designated area

- Replace with a full bottle and secure in position, ensuring the arrow on the bottle base is pointing downwards. Ideally this should be a two man lift

- Reconnect the fuel line to the gas bottle

- Open the gas bottle valve

- Ensure the seal is sound and that there is no gas leakage, if leakage is found close the valve and report to your supervisor

- Ensure there is adequate ventilation

- A fire extinguisher must be present

- Personnal protective equipment must be worn at all times

Note: If leaving a gas powered truck overnight or for long periods of time, close the gas bottle service valve.

Diesel/petrol powered trucks

Always follow these refuelling procedures:

- Refuel only at recognised refuelling points
- Park the truck correctly
- Ensure the engine is switched off and remove the key
- Fill with the correct fuel
- Do not overfill the tank – leave room for fuel expansion
- Replace the filler cap securely
- Clear away any fuel spills
- Ensure there is adequate ventilation
- A fire extinguisher must be present
- Personnal protective equipment must be worn at all times

Note: If the tank is kept at least half full it will help reduce condensation build up, which can lead to corrosion.

Remember!
No smoking or naked lights in the refuelling area – this applies to all types of fuel.

Fork lift truck safety

Summary

You should now know how to minimise the risk of accidents by following the correct procedures for:

- Pre-use checks
- Reporting faults
- Using seat belts
- Using attachments
- Battery care and charging
- Refuelling

Remember!

Don't be careless with any of these routine checks or operations – pride comes before a fall!

Safe driving

Just think how many strong people it would take to lift some of the loads you handle with your fork lift. That's how much power you have at your finger tips!

Now think what damage that power and weight could do as a result of just a moment's loss of concentration or a silly mistake by the driver.

The rules in this section are not petty regulations to keep the inspectors happy. Someone's life – perhaps yours – may depend on you obeying these rules and guidelines.

We'll cover:

- General rules for safe driving
- Driving on slopes
- Drink and drugs
- Public highways

General rules for safe driving

It's virtually impossible to legislate for all possibilities, so the following rules don't cover everything. To help you remember them, we've grouped them under these headings:

- Driving/operating conditions
- Be sensible and obey the rules
- Keep a look out
- If you can't see
- Stay in control
- Park properly

Fork lift truck safety

- Operate correctly
- Take care of yourself

Remember!
Always use your common sense in any situation.
If in doubt, stop and ask your supervisor.

Driving/operating conditions

Take extra care when operating in adverse conditions
such as:

- Ice
- Snow
- Rain
- Poor light
- Bright sunlight

Concentrate

Never do anything which could mar the concentration
or physical ability to control the truck,
for example:

- Eating
- Drinking
- Using a mobile phone
- Smoking

Be sensible; obey the rules

- Never carry
  passengers on a
  fork lift truck

MENTOR

- Don't get involved in horseplay of any type – always concentrate on the job in hand!

- Obey all signs and travel direction restrictions

- In no circumstances should you add extra counterweight to a truck to enable it to lift a heavier load than it's plated for

Keep a look out
- Look carefully all around you before moving

- Keep looking in the direction of travel

- Always look up to ensure sufficient clearance before raising the forks/load

- Make sure you have sufficient overhead clearance for doorways, pipes, lights, cables, etc

- Although you're aware of the large front and rear end swing that occurs when operating the truck, not all pedestrians are! So don't rely on them to keep far enough away from the truck. It's the driver's responsibility to ensure the safety of pedestrians – keep a look out for them at all times and give them a wide berth

If you can't see
- Never drive forwards with a load obstructing your view – drive in reverse instead, unless you're going up a slope and then you'll need someone to guide you

When approaching a blind corner:

- Slow down and manoeuvre slowly
- Be prepared to stop
- Be aware of the potential hazards of pedestrians and other trucks etc.
- Give several short sharp blasts on the horn to warn of your presence

Stay in control

- Keep at least one hand on the steering wheel at all times whilst the truck is moving
- Always travel at a speed suited to the load and the general conditions
- Avoid making sharp turns or sudden stops
- Leave a minimum separation gap of three truck lengths when following another truck down an aisle
- When crossing speed bumps, railway lines or shallow gullies, travel slowly and cross diagonally, one wheel at a time

Park properly

■ Make sure you always park the truck safely:

- With key removed to prevent unauthorised use

- Not causing an obstruction

- Away from blind spots, doors, loading bays, emergency exits, fire fighting equipment, electricity panels, etc.

- Not on a slope

■ If you have to reposition a load by getting off the truck and manually adjusting it: place the truck in the safe park position, switch off and remove the key before getting off

■ If you come across debris on the floor: stop, park safely and remove it. The next driver may not spot it, resulting in an accident

Operate correctly

- If the side shift facility has been used, always return it to the central position after use

- Never lift a load using only one fork arm

- Always operate the hydraulic controls smoothly – jerky operation can dislodge the load or even tip the truck over!

- Do not push or drag loads along the ground

- Do not carry divisible loads that are higher than the fork carriage or load backrest extension

- Do not operate with insecure or unsafe loads

- Do not use defective pallets or stillages

- Take extra care when the forks stick out beyond the pallet or load

- You have been trained to handle palletised loads during your training course
- If you are required to handle something unfamiliar, consult your supervisor and ensure the load can be made safe for handling - never handle an unsafe load

- Do not allow anyone to be raised by the lift truck unless they are in an approved work platform

Fork lift truck safety

Take care of yourself

- Never allow any part of your body to protrude outside of the cab of the truck whilst in operation

- When mounting and dismounting:
    - face the truck
    - use the hand grips and steps provided
    - look all around for hazards
    - get on and off the truck under control and one foot at a time
    - do not jump

Finally, if your truck is about to tip over:

- Do not try to jump off
- Hold on tightly and brace yourself
- Lean away from the point of impact

MENTOR

Driving on slopes

Always take great care when driving on a slope, as there's a greater chance of an accident.

Remember these guidelines:

- Drive slowly and use the brakes gently
- Never turn on a slope, even with an unladen truck
- Always drive directly up or down the slope, never at a diagonal
- Keep the forks as low as possible, with back tilt applied, to reduce the truck's centre of gravity
- Ideally, the forks should face uphill if the truck is laden and downhill if the truck is unladen

- Driving in this way aids stability, traction and adhesion (meaning the truck is less likely to tip over or skid)
- When it's not possible to drive up and down the incline with the forks positioned as above (for example when loading a vehicle using a portable loading ramp), go down the ramp with greater care

Drink and drugs

The law considers a fork lift truck to be a motor vehicle. This means that an operator who is found to be operating a truck whilst under the influence of drink or drugs can be prosecuted.

This doesn't just apply to public highways, but also to factories and warehouses etc. It also follows that if a manager/

supervisor were aware of a driver operating whilst under the influence, and allowed them to continue operating, they could also be prosecuted.

Public highways

Some of the main rules that apply to using fork lifts on public roads are:

- The truck must be registered and licensed
- The minimum insurance requirement is third party liability at all times
- The truck should display a number plate on the rear of the truck or on both sides
- The driver must hold a full category B (car) driving licence
- The driver must be properly trained on the truck type being driven in accordance with the HASAWA 1974
- The permitted size/capacity of the truck depends on the age of the driver

- The load should not project forwards more than two metres
- Appropriate lighting must be fitted to the truck if it is to be used during the hours of darkness

Remember!
Over the pavement loading and unloading counts as road use.

Summary

Driving a fork lift truck is a great responsibility because you have so much power at your finger tips. Make sure you use that power safely by always following the guidelines and rules in this section for:

- General safe driving
- Driving on slopes
- Drink and drugs
- Public highways

Loading and unloading

Loading and unloading are key operations for fork lift drivers. It's what you do all the time. But familiarity can breed contempt. Lack of care, thought and attention leads to accidents.

If this seems a bit 'unpalletable', take a load off your mind by reading the guidelines in this section – and then stick to them!

We'll cover:

- ■ General rules for loading and unloading
- ■ Loading
- ■ Unloading
- ■ Pallet and load assessment
- ■ Stacking
- ■ Undercutting
- ■ Racking systems

General rules

If you are loading/unloading another lorry/vehicle, the driver of that vehicle is responsible for the safety and security of his/her load, so you should follow their instructions. However, you still need to learn and stick to a number of basic rules:

- ■ Make sure the vehicle is parked correctly and the driver is aware you are about to start loading/ unloading
- ■ Ensure the vehicle's engine is switched off, the key removed, and brakes applied. Chock the wheels if necessary

- Make sure the vehicle bed is free of debris and sufficiently strong to take the load
- Some uncoupled semi-trailers may need a jack or prop placed under the front end to prevent them tipping over during loading/unloading

Loading

You should normally start loading at the front of the vehicle and work backwards on alternate sides of the vehicle, as shown on this diagram:

Make sure that:

- You load in delivery order, which means first on is last off. The diagram shows the pallets numbered in their order of loading (alternate sides)
- Pallets/loads are tight against each other to prevent slipping and sliding during transit and to maximise the load that the vehicle can carry
- You load from both sides and never push a load from one side of the vehicle to the other

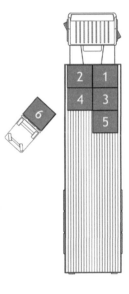

You may need to disregard the rule of even weight distribution so as to achieve correct axle weight.

If loading from the ground, check there is adequate access on both sides of the vehicle on firm ground, free from potholes or manhole covers, etc.

If loading from a loading bay, double check that the vehicle brakes are applied, as the large live forces applied to the vehicle as the fork lift drives onto it could cause it to move.

Remember!

Always double check that the bed of the vehicle and the bridge plate or dock leveler are secure and strong enough to take the weight of the truck and the load.

Unloading

The diagram below shows a vehicle being unloaded.
The pallets are numbered in the order of unloading
(alternate sides). You should normally start from the
back of the vehicle and work forwards.

If unloading from the ground:

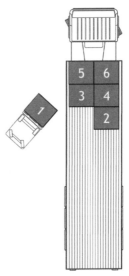

■ Check there is
adequate access on
both sides of the
vehicle on firm ground,
free from potholes or
manhole covers, etc.

■ Take loads off from
alternate sides of the
vehicle – otherwise
the vehicle may lean
to one side so much
that it's impossible to
insert the forks into a
pallet or other load.
In extreme cases the
vehicle may tip over

Remember!

If using a pedestrian controlled truck, you
should normally load/unload vehicles in
pedestrian mode.

Pallet and load assessment

Before picking up any load, you need to check the procedure will be safe in several ways:

Weight of load

Make sure the weight of the load falls within the rated capacity of the truck. If in doubt, consult your supervisor.

A label with the words '**load net weight**' refers to the weight of the load alone.

A label bearing the wording '**load gross weight**' refers to the combined weight of the load, packaging and pallet.

Load centre

Ensure the load centre and weight of the load fall within the rated capacity of the truck.

Condition of pallet

Check the pallet is in good condition and not liable to break and shed the load on lifting.

Condition of the load

Make sure the load is secure and is not likely to slip when being lifted and transported.

Ensure the weight of the load is evenly distributed on the pallet, so both forks will take an even weight.

Size of the load

Ensure the load is not too large to travel the route to its resting place and that it will fit in its intended location.

Forks

Check that the forks will not protrude beyond the pallet – this may dislodge a load in the next bay or damage something just beyond the pallet.

Corner post pallets/stillages

There are many types of corner post pallets. Most are made of metal with either solid sides or wire mesh sides. They have a receiving device (cup or socket) on the bottom of each corner and a stubby leg at the top of each corner (or the other way round).

There will be a limit placed on how many high you can stack these, determined by the construction of the pallet and the load carried. Ensure you know this limit before stacking – and don't exceed it.

Remember!

As the truck forks and the corner post pallet are both metal, there is a greater risk of the pallet slipping off the forks, so you should normally use full back tilt when transporting the load.

Stacking

Before stacking or de-stacking any load, you must make sure it's safe to do so by checking the following:

Pallet positioning in racking

In a racking system there should be a 50-75mm gap between pallets and/or uprights, so that you have a view to ensure no snagging on depositing and removing.

There should also be a 25-50mm overhang on the front of the racking to:

■ Distribute the load weight evenly on the racking beams

■ Help stop the load being shunted through the racking if the pallet is inadvertently nudged by forks that are too high or too low

Free standing pallet stacking

Be very careful when bulk stacking – it's crucial to position pallets exactly on top of each other to prevent the stack toppling over!

Do not exceed the agreed maximum height – this could result in crushing of the lower loads, again leading to the stack collapsing.

Undercutting

This means not inserting the forks fully into the pallet up to the fork heels. It is sometimes necessary to 'undercut' a load to enable an initial lift, e.g. where it's impossible to move close enough to the load to insert the forks fully.

If you have to do this, follow these procedures:

Safe working load
Because the load centre distance is greater, the safe working load will be less. Make sure the rated capacity of the truck can cope with the increased load centre distance before lifting.

Picking up
- Insert the forks as far as possible into the pallet. They must enter at least two thirds of the way in
- Gently lift the pallet just enough to make sure the load is stable
- If the load is not stable, gently lower it back down and report the problem to your manager or supervisor
- If the load is stable, slowly reverse far enough to set the load down
- Once the load is safely on the ground, reposition the forks so the heels just touch the pallet
- Re-lift the pallet and continue to transport the load as normal

Setting down
- Having transported the pallet as normal, place it on the ground
- Reposition the forks so they do not protrude beyond the pallet. They need to be inserted at least two thirds of the way into the pallet
- Gently lift the load a few inches and check that it's stable. If it is, continue and stack in the normal way. If it's not stable, gently lower, reposition the forks and try again

Racking systems

All racking should be checked regularly – both for damage and correct stacking. The points and diagram cover the main things you should check for:

- Uprights are securely fastened to the floor

- Uprights and cross members are free from damage

- Securing pins are in place

- Pallets are correctly located

- Pallets containing many small boxes or items are secured by shrink wrap, banding or another method to ensure they will not be easily dislodged from the pallet

- Pallets are free from damage

Remember!

Do not use defective racking or pallets. Report any damage immediately.

Uniformly Distributed Load (UDL)

Just as it's important to check that the racking is capable of taking the weight placed on it, it's also vital to space the loads evenly along the width of available racking between the uprights. The diagram below shows this:

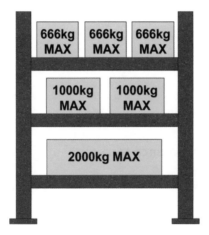

Summary

We hope this section was not too heavy! You should now understand the guidelines and rules for:

- ◼ Loading
- ◼ Unloading
- ◼ Pallet and load assessment
- ◼ Stacking
- ◼ Undercutting
- ◼ Racking systems

Operating different types of truck

In this section we'll look at stacking and de-stacking procedures and a few other rules for:

- Counterbalance trucks
- Reach trucks
- Pivot steer trucks
- Side loading trucks

We'll cover pedestrian operated trucks separately in the next section.

Counterbalance trucks

Stacking
You should follow the procedure shown in the next eight diagrams:

Step 1

- Approach the designated stacking location in the safe travel position
- Turn through 90°, if required, to face the location
- Stop with the front of the load 150mm from the racking or bulk stacking area and centrally positioned
- Apply the parking brake and select neutral

Step 2

■ Level the forks. (If lifting to a high level, you can make a further check with the forks at eye level)

Step 3

■ Check above to make sure there is clear headroom before lifting

■ Lift the load so the bottom of the pallet is 50-75mm above the racking (or the load/pallet beneath if bulk stacking)

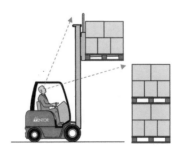

Step 4

- Select forward gear, look carefully all around you and release the parking brake

- Move forwards gently, under control, making any
  small steering corrections necessary to position the pallet correctly in its intended location. Also check to ensure the base of the mast does not contact the racking or stack

- Remember to position the pallet correctly with a 50-75mm safety gap on each side of the load and, if stacking in racking, allow the pallet to overhang the front of the racking by 25-50mm

- If bulk stacking, make sure you position the load exactly on top of the load beneath, keeping the stack perfectly upright and level

- Apply the parking brake and select neutral

Step 5

- Lower the load smoothly, under control
- Position the forks at a height to clear the pallet without fouling on withdrawal

Step 6

- Select reverse gear, look carefully all around you and release the parking brake

- Reverse away, looking in the direction of travel, with occasional checks to make sure the forks do not rub on the pallet on withdrawal

- If it looks like the forks may rub on withdrawal, stop and make the necessary adjustment – but carry out the correct procedure of parking brake and neutral before using the hydraulic controls

- Stop with the fork tips 150mm away from the load

- Apply the parking brake and select neutral

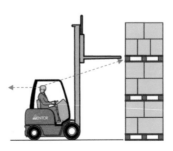

Step 7

■ Lower forks, under control

Step 8

■ Place in the safe travel position

De-stacking with a counterbalance truck

Follow the procedure shown in the next eight diagrams:

Step 1

- Approach the designated stacking location in the safe travel position.

- Turn through 90°, if required, to face the location. Stop with the fork tips 150mm from the racking or bulk stacking area and centrally positioned

- Apply the parking brake and select neutral

Step 2

- Level the forks. (If lifting to a high level, you can make a further check with the forks at eye level)

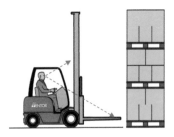

Step 3

■ Check above to make sure you have clear headroom before lifting

■ Lift the forks to the correct height to enter the pallet cleanly

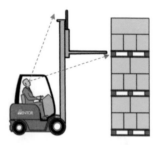

Step 4

■ Select forward gear, look carefully all around you and release the parking brake

■ Move forwards slowly, under control, making any slight steering adjustments needed until the fork heels gently kiss the pallet. Also check that the base of the mast does not contact the racking or stack

■ If it looks like the forks will rub on the pallet on entry, stop and make the necessary adjustments, but carry out the correct procedure of parking brake and neutral before operating the hydraulic controls

■ Apply the parking brake and select neutral

Step 5

■ Check above to make sure there is clear headroom before lifting. Pay particular attention to the backrest extension, if fitted

■ Lift the pallet approximately 50-75mm. If at this point the truck/forks/load dip forwards slightly due to a heavy load, apply a slight amount of back tilt to level the forks again so the load is level when you withdraw it

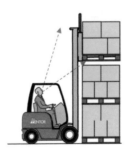

Step 6

- Select reverse gear, look carefully all around you and release the parking brake

- Reverse away, looking in the direction of travel with checks to ensure the pallet/load does not foul on the racking or adjacent loads on withdrawal. Make any slight steering adjustments, as necessary, to avoid this

- Stop with the load 150mm away from the racking or bulk stack

- Apply the parking brake and select neutral

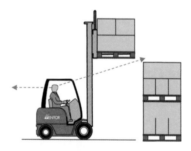

Step 7

- Lower the load, under control

Step 8

■ Place in the safe travel position

Reach trucks

Stacking

You should follow the procedure shown in the next 10 diagrams:

Step 1

■ Approach the designated stacking location in the safe travel position

■ Turn through 90°, if required, to face the location. Stop with the front of the load 150mm from the racking or bulk stacking area, and centrally positioned

■ Apply the parking brake and select neutral

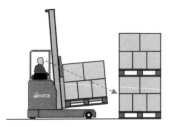

Step 2

- Level the forks (if lifting to a high level, you can make a further check with the forks at eye level)

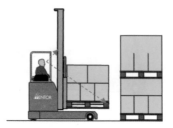

Step 3

- Check above to make sure you have clear headroom before lifting

- Lift the load so the bottom of the pallet is 50-75mm above the racking (or the load/pallet beneath if bulk stacking)

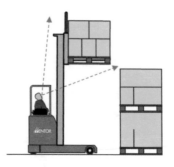

Step 4

- Select forward gear, look carefully all around you and release the parking brake

- Move forwards gently, under control, making any small steering corrections as necessary to position the pallet correctly in its intended location

- Stop when the reach legs are about 50mm from the racking or bulk stack

- Apply the parking brake and select neutral

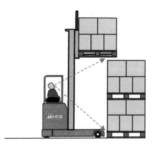

Step 5

- Extend the reach and position the load correctly

- If at this point the reach is fully extended and the pallet is not far enough into the racking (or bulk stack) to be positioned correctly, move forwards until it is in the correct position

Remember!
Keep any travel with reach extended to an absolute minimum.

- Remember to position the pallet correctly with a 50-75mm safety gap on each side of the load and, if stacking in racking, allow the pallet to overhang the front of the racking by 25-50mm

- If bulk stacking, position the load exactly on top of the load beneath, keeping the stack perfectly upright and level

- Re-apply the parking brake and select neutral

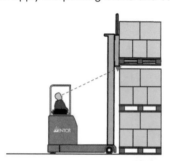

Step 6

- Lower the load smoothly, under control, onto the racking or bulk stack

- Position the forks at a height to clear the pallet without fouling on withdrawal

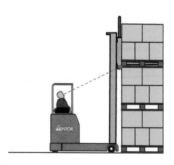

Step 7

■ Fully retract the reach, checking to make sure the forks do not foul the pallet on withdrawal

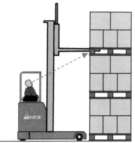

Step 8

■ Select reverse gear, look carefully all around you and release the parking brake

■ Reverse away, looking in the direction of travel with occasional checks to ensure the forks do not rub on the pallet on withdrawal

■ If it looks like the forks may rub the pallet on withdrawal, stop and make the necessary adjustment, but carry out the correct procedure of parking brake and neutral before operating the hydraulic controls

■ Stop with the fork tips 150mm away from the load

■ Apply the parking brake and select neutral

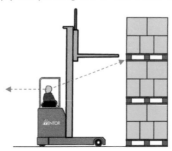

Step 9

■ Lower the forks, under control

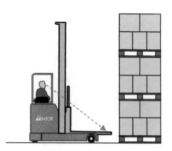

Step 10

■ Place in the safe travel position

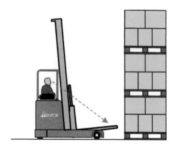

De-stacking with a reach truck

Follow the procedure shown in the next 10 diagrams:

Step 1

■ Approach the designated stacking location in the safe travel position

■ Turn through 90°, if required, to face the location – stop with the fork tips 150mm from the racking or bulk stacking area and centrally positioned

■ Apply the parking brake and select neutral

Step 2

■ Level the forks. (If lifting to a high level, you can make a further check with the forks at eye level)

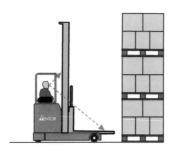

Step 3

■ Check above to ensure you have clear headroom before lifting

■ Lift the forks to the correct height to enter the pallet cleanly

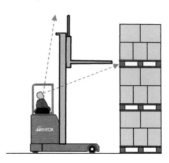

Step 4

■ Select forward gear, look carefully all around you and release the parking brake

■ Move forwards slowly, under control, making any slight steering corrections as necessary. Check to ensure the forks do not rub the pallet on entry and stop when the reach legs are approximately 50mm from the load

■ If it looks like the forks will rub on the pallet on entry, stop and make the necessary adjustments, but carry out the correct procedure of parking brake and neutral before operating the hydraulic controls

■ Apply the parking brake and select neutral

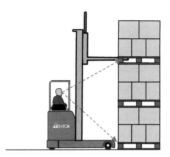

Step 5

■ Extend the reach until the fork heels gently kiss the pallet

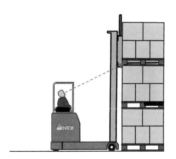

Fork lift truck safety

Step 6

- Check above to make sure you have clear headroom before lifting – pay particular attention to the backrest extension, if fitted

- Lift the pallet approximately 50-75mm. If at this point the truck/forks/load dip forwards slightly due to a heavy load, apply a slight amount of back tilt to level the forks again so that the load is level as you withdraw it

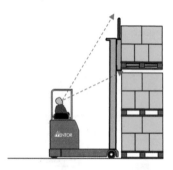

Step 7

- Fully retract the reach, checking that the pallet/load does not foul on the racking or adjacent loads

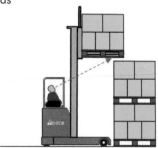

MENTOR

Step 8

- Select reverse gear, look carefully all around you and release the parking brake

- Reverse away, looking in the direction of travel. Check that the pallet/load does not foul on the racking or adjacent loads on withdrawal, and make any slight steering adjustments, as necessary, to avoid this

- Stop with the load 150mm away from the racking

- Apply the parking brake and select neutral

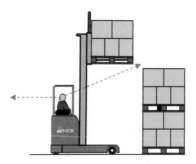

Step 9

- Lower the load, under control

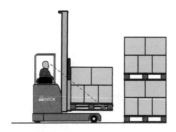

Step 10

■ Place in the safe travel position

Extra rules for reach trucks

■ Never travel with the reach extended – always adopt the safe travel position

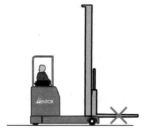

■ Always make sure you have lifted the load clear of the reach legs before retracting the reach

Pivot steer trucks

Stacking

If you have to carry out a turn to enable stacking there are two different methods that can be employed.

Method 1 is recommended where the aisle is sufficiently wide enough to enable a full turn, within the aisle, at ground level to address the racking.

Method 2 can be used where the aisle is narrower and a full turn at ground level within the aisle is not possible.

If you are driving directly forwards into the stacking location and reversing straight out, follow the same procedure as for stacking with a counterbalance truck (see pages 74-78).

Method 1

Stacking with a pivot steer truck

If you have to turn 90° to stack, follow the procedure shown in the next six diagrams:

Step 1

- Approach the designated stacking location in the safe travel position, driving on the opposite side of the aisle to the one you will be stacking in

- Stop when the front wheel is opposite the centre of the stacking location

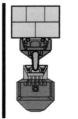

Fork lift truck safety

Step 2

- Pivot the truck to face the location, stopping with the front of the load 150mm from the racking or bulk stacking area and centrally positioned

- Apply the parking brake and select neutral

- Level the forks. (If lifting to a high level, you can make a further check with the forks at eye level)

- Check above to ensure you have clear headroom before lifting

- Lift the load so the bottom of the pallet is 50-75mm above the racking (or the load/pallet beneath if bulk stacking)

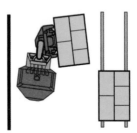

Step 3

- Select forward gear, look carefully all around you and release the parking brake

- Move forwards slowly and start to unwind the steering whilst moving the load into position. Keep the load parallel with the side of the racking or neighbouring stacked pallet

MENTOR

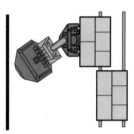

Step 4

■ When the load is correctly positioned, apply the parking brake and select neutral

■ Remember to position the pallet with a 50-75mm safety gap on each side of the load and, if stacking in racking, allow the pallet to overhang the front of the racking by 25-50mm

■ If bulk stacking, position the load exactly on top of the load beneath, keeping the stack perfectly upright and level

■ Lower the load smoothly, under control, onto the racking or bulk stack

■ Position the forks at a height to clear the pallet without fouling on withdrawal

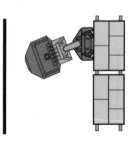

Step 5

- Select reverse gear, look carefully all around you and release the parking brake

- Reverse away, looking both in the direction of travel and at the forks as they withdraw from the pallet. Adjust the steering to keep the forks parallel with the pallet all the time

- If it looks like the forks may rub on withdrawal, stop and make the necessary adjustment. Carry out the correct procedure of parking brake and neutral before using the hydraulic controls

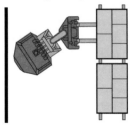

Step 6

- Once the forks are clear of the pallet, stop and gently unwind the steering to bring the truck into line

- Apply the parking brake and select neutral

- Lower forks under control, and place in the safe travel position

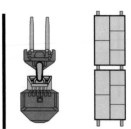

De-stacking with a pivot steer truck

If you are driving directly forwards into the de-stacking location and then reversing straight back, follow the same procedure as when de-stacking with a counterbalance truck (see pages 79-83).

If you have to turn 90° to de-stack, follow the procedure shown in the next seven diagrams:

Step 1

■ Approach the designated de-stacking location in the safe travel position, driving on the opposite side of the aisle to the one you will be de-stacking in

■ Stop when the front wheel is opposite the centre of the pallet to be de-stacked

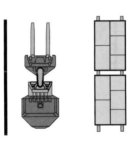

Step 2

- Pivot the truck to face the pallet, stopping with the fork tips 150mm from the racking or bulk stacking area and centrally positioned
- Apply the parking brake and select neutral
- Level the forks. (If lifting to a high level, you can make a further check with the forks at eye level)
- Check above to ensure you have clear headroom before lifting
- Lift the forks to the correct height to enter the pallet cleanly

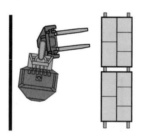

Step 3

- Select forward gear, look carefully all around you and release the parking brake
- Move forwards slowly, under control, unwinding the steering as needed to keep the forks centrally positioned

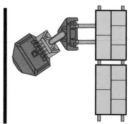

Step 4

- Keep going, adjusting the steering to keep the forks centrally positioned, until the fork heels gently kiss the pallet

- If it looks like the forks will rub on the pallet on entry, stop and make the necessary adjustments. Carry out the correct procedure of parking brake and neutral before operating the hydraulic controls

- Apply the parking brake and select neutral

- Check above to ensure you have clear headroom before lifting – pay particular attention to the backrest extension, if fitted

- Lift the pallet approximately 50-75mm. If at this point the truck/forks/load dip forwards slightly due to a heavy load, apply a slight amount of back tilt to level the forks again so the load will be level as you withdraw it

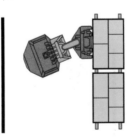

Step 5

- Select reverse gear, look carefully all around you and release the parking brake

- Reverse away, looking both in the direction of travel and the load to ensure it does not foul on the racking or adjacent loads on withdrawal. Make any slight steering adjustments as necessary to avoid this

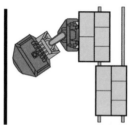

Step 6

- Stop with the load sufficiently clear of the racking or bulk stack to turn the pallet

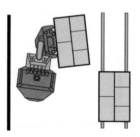

Step 7

- Gently unwind the steering to bring the truck into line
- Apply the parking brake and select neutral
- Lower the load, under control, and place in the safe travel position

Method 2

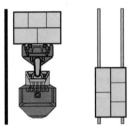

Stacking to the right side of an aisle

> ## Remember
> This method is only to be used
> on firm level ground

Step 1

- Approach the designated stacking location in safe travel position and with the left side of the truck, or load, approximately 200mm from the left hand racking

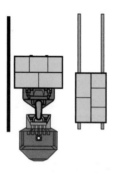

Step 2

- About 1 metre before reaching the chosen stacking location, steer slightly left so that when the front right wheel is opposite the right corner of the chosen stacking location the front left wheel, or the load, is approx 50mm away from the racking on the left

- Stop, apply the parking brake and select neutral

- Sideshift fully to the right and level the forks. (if lifting to a high level, you can make a further check with the forks at eye level)

- Check above to ensure you have clear headroom before lifting the forks

- Lift the forks to the required height

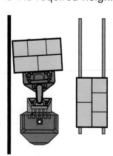

Step 3

- Select forward gear, look carefully all around you and release the parking brake

- Simultaneously turn towards the chosen pallet stacking location while feathering forward traction. (the axle should rotate around the stationary right wheel)

- Once the pallet begins to enter the stacking location feather sideshift to the left while straightening steering to keep the pallet flush with the racking and the adjacent pallets

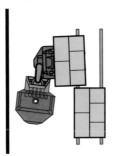

Step 4

- Continue forwards until the pallet is correctly positioned within the racking.

- Remember that a correctly positioned pallet has a 50-75mm safety gap down either side of it and, in most cases, a 25-50mm overhang on the front of the racking. However in some very narrow aisle applications pallets may be stacked without a 25-50mm front edge overhang. Observe how other pallets are stacked within the racking and stack accordingly

- Apply the parking brake and select neutral.

- Gently lower the pallet to rest on the racking beams

- Position the forks at the correct height to be able to withdraw from the pallet without catching

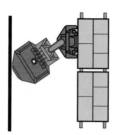

Step 5

- Select reverse gear. look carefully all around you and start to slowly reverse while steering to the right and feathering sideshift to the right to keep the forks from contacting the pallet on the way out.

- Continue to withdraw from the pallet while making observational checks to the rear and the forks

- Continue in this way until the forks are sufficiently clear to be able to turn

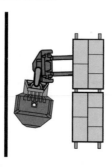

Step 6

- Slowly and smoothly unwind the steering to bring the truck in line.
- Apply the parking brake
- Centralise the side shift
- Smoothly lower the forks to safe travel position
- Apply stabilising back tilt

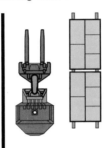

De-stacking from the right side of an aisle

Remember
This method is only to be used
on firm level ground

Step 1

- Approach the designated de-stacking location in safe travel position and with the left side of the truck approximately 200mm from the left hand racking

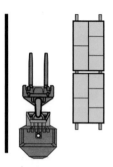

Step 2

- About 1 metre before reaching the chosen pallet, steer slightly left so that when the front right wheel is opposite the right corner of the chosen pallet face, the front left wheel is approx 50mm away from the left hand racking

- Stop, apply the parking brake and select neutral

- Sideshift fully to the right and level the forks. (if lifting to a high level, you can make a further check with the forks at eye level)

- Check above to ensure you have clear headroom before lifting the forks

- Lift the forks to the required height

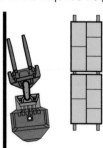

Step 3

- Select forward gear, look carefully all around you and release the parking brake

- Simultaneously turn towards the chosen pallet while feathering forward traction. (the axle should rotate around the stationary right wheel)

- Once the forks begin to enter the pallet feather the sideshift to the left while straightening the steering

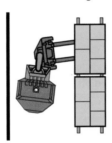

Step 4

- Continue moving forwards and once the forks have fully entered the pallet they should be centrally located and the sideshift mostly, if not fully, to the left

- Apply the parking brake and select neutral

- Check above to ensure clear headroom and lift the load just clear of the beams. If at this point the truck/forks/load dip forwards slightly due to a heavy load, apply a slight amount of back tilt to level the forks again.

  Note: Applying an amount of back tilt at this point can help pallet extraction in higher racking, but be careful of the rear of the pallet fouling the upper racking

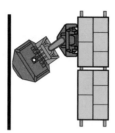

Step 5

- Engage reverse gear, look carefully all around you and release the parking brake

- Slowly reverse while steering to the right and feathering sideshift to the right

- Keep the pallet square to the racking and adjacent loads as you reverse away while observing rear clearance and pallet movement.

- Continue in this way until the pallet is sufficiently clear to be able to turn

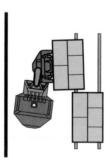

Step 6

- Slowly and smoothly unwind the steering to bring the truck in line.
- Apply the parking brake
- Centralise the side shift
- Smoothly lower the load to safe travel position
- Apply stabilising back tilt

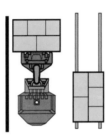

Remember

Method 2 is for stacking and de-stacking from the right of an aisle if stacking or de-stacking from the left reverse the positioning

Side loading trucks

> # Remember!
>
> The counterbalance, reach and pivot steer trucks we have looked at so far deal mainly with palletised loads.
>
> Side loading lift trucks can also deal with palletised loads. However, they will mainly be used for handling longer loads such as lengths of timber and steel section or tubing.
>
> The following stacking and de-stacking procedures are shown with the truck handling secure banded lengths of timber, which can be stacked and de-stacked with forks level due to the rigidity of the load.
>
> With unsecured/loose loads, it is important that tilt is used to help maintain load stability.

Stacking

Follow the procedure shown in the next six diagrams:

Step 1

- Approach the designated stacking location in the safe travel position

- Stop the truck when the load is in line with, parallel to, and the correct distance away from the intended racking or bulk stacking location

- Apply the parking brake and select neutral

- Lower the stabilising jacks if fitted and required, ensuring they are hard down on firm ground

- Level the forks. On some trucks the forks will tilt independently of the bed of the truck whereas on other trucks the whole truck bed will tilt. (If lifting to a high level, you can make a further check with the forks at eye level)

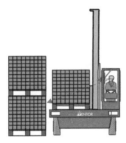

Step 2

- Check above to ensure you have clear headroom
before lifting

- Lift the load so the bottom of the pallet is 50-75mm above the racking (or the load/pallet beneath if bulk stacking)

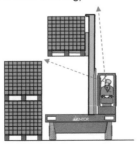

Step 3

■ Traverse the load out until it is correctly positioned, taking care not to dislodge other loads

■ Remember to position the pallet with a 50-75mm safety gap on each side of the load and, if stacking in racking, allow the pallet to overhang the front of the racking by 25-50mm

■ If bulk stacking, position the load exactly on top of the load beneath, keeping the stack perfectly upright and level

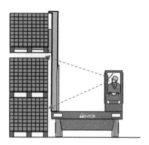

Step 4

■ Lower the pallet/load smoothly, under control, onto the racking or bulk stack

■ Position the forks at a height to clear the pallet/ load without fouling on withdrawal

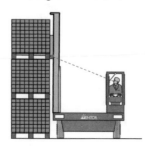

Step 5

■ Traverse the mast fully back, checking to ensure the forks do not foul the pallet/load on withdrawal

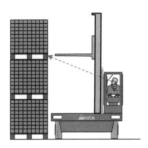

Step 6

■ Lower the forks, under control, and place in the safe travel position

■ Raise the stabilising jacks, if fitted and in use

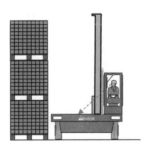

De-stacking with a side loading truck

Follow the procedure shown in the next six diagrams:

Step 1

- Approach the designated de-stacking location in the safe travel position

- Stop the truck when the forks are in line with, parallel to, and the correct distance away from the intended racking or bulk stacking location

- Apply the parking brake and select neutral

- Lower the stabilising jacks, if fitted and required, ensuring they are hard down on firm ground

- Level the forks. On some trucks the forks will tilt independently of the bed of the truck, whereas on other trucks the whole truck bed will tilt. (If lifting to a high level a further check can be made with the forks at eye level)

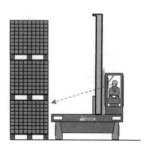

Step 2

- Check above to ensure you have clear headroom before lifting
- Lift the forks to the correct height to enter the pallet/load cleanly

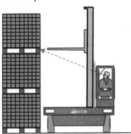

Step 3

- Traverse out until the fork heels gently kiss the pallet/load

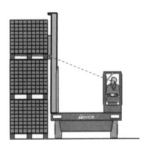

Step 4

■ Check above to ensure you have clear headroom before lifting – pay particular attention to the backrest extension, if fitted

■ Lift the pallet/load approximately 50-75mm. If at this point the truck/forks/load dip slightly due to a heavy load, apply a slight amount of back tilt to level the forks again so the load is level as you withdraw it

Step 5

■ Traverse the load back fully, checking to ensure the pallet/load does not foul on the racking or adjacent loads

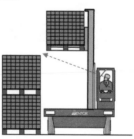

Step 6

- Lower the load smoothly, under control onto the deck of the truck

- Position the forks in the safe travel position

- Raise the stabilising jacks, if fitted and used

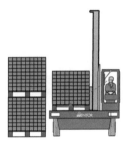

Extra rules for side loaders

- Make sure the load is lifted clear of the deck before traversing in

- Failing to lift high enough can result in a lost load and/or damage to the truck and load

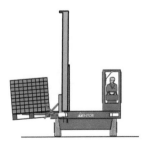

Fork lift truck safety

- Make sure the load is lifted clear of the deck before traversing out
- Do not push the load along the deck – this can damage both the truck and the load

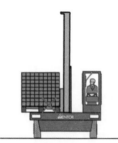

- If the truck is fitted with stabilising jacks, do not lift loads greater than the un-jacked capacity of the truck without using the jacks
- When using the stabilising jacks, ensure they are fully deployed on firm ground

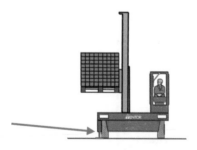

MENTOR

■ Never travel with the mast traversed out – always
adopt the safe travel position

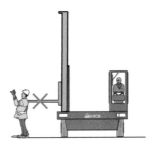

Summary

In this section we've covered stacking and
de-stacking procedures and a few other rules for:

■ Counterbalance trucks
■ Reach trucks
■ Pivot steer trucks
■ Side loading trucks

You will have noticed many similarities and a few
important differences between these procedures.
Rather than try to learn these procedures all in one
go, try to become familiar with whichever type of
truck you are currently using. Whenever you use a
different type of truck, look up the relevant section
again and pay particular attention to any differences
in the procedure.

Pedestrian operated trucks

In this final section we take a look at the various types of pedestrian operated trucks. We'll cover:

- Basic components
- General safe driving rules
- Principles of stability for pedestrian stacking trucks
- Pallet and load assessment
- Operating procedures

Basic components

The following three diagrams show the basic components of the:

- Pedestrian operated powered pallet truck
- Low level order picker
- Pedestrian operated powered pallet stacker

Pedestrian operated powered pallet truck

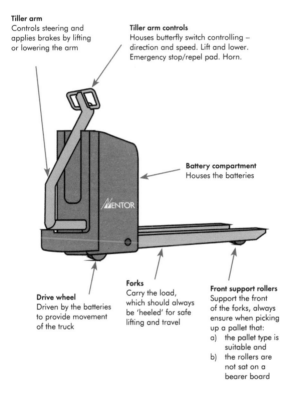

Tiller arm
Controls steering and applies brakes by lifting or lowering the arm

Tiller arm controls
Houses butterfly switch controlling – direction and speed. Lift and lower. Emergency stop/repel pad. Horn.

Battery compartment
Houses the batteries

Drive wheel
Driven by the batteries to provide movement of the truck

Forks
Carry the load, which should always be 'heeled' for safe lifting and travel

Front support rollers
Support the front of the forks, always ensure when picking up a pallet that:
a) the pallet type is suitable and
b) the rollers are not sat on a bearer board

Note: Some models will have a flip down platform and travel guards. NOT SHOWN ON THIS ILLUSTRATION.

Low level order picker

Tiller arm controls
Houses butterfly switch controlling –
Direction and speed. Lift and lower.
Emergency stop/repel pad. Horn.

Backrest
Some truck types will
also have a small
flip-down platform to
enable the operator
to reach higher
stacked goods

Tiller arm
Controls steering and
applies brakes by lifting
or lowering the arm

Stand in platform
Operator position,
normally with
'deadman' foot pad

Forks
Carry the load,
which should always
be 'heeled' for safe
lifting and travel

Drive wheel
Driven by the batteries
to provide movement
of the truck

Battery compartment
Houses the batteries

Front support rollers
Support the front
of the forks, always
ensure when picking
up a pallet that:
a) the pallet type is
   suitable and
b) the rollers are not
   sat on a bearer
   board

Pedestrian operated powered pallet stacker

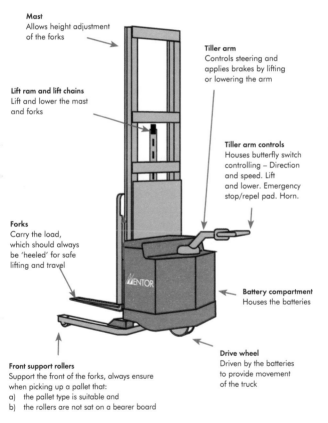

Mast
Allows height adjustment
of the forks

Tiller arm
Controls steering and
applies brakes by lifting
or lowering the arm

Lift ram and lift chains
Lift and lower the mast
and forks

Tiller arm controls
Houses butterfly switch
controlling – Direction
and speed. Lift
and lower. Emergency
stop/repel pad. Horn.

Forks
Carry the load,
which should always
be 'heeled' for safe
lifting and travel

MENTOR

Battery compartment
Houses the batteries

Drive wheel
Driven by the batteries
to provide movement
of the truck

Front support rollers
Support the front of the forks, always ensure
when picking up a pallet that:
a)   the pallet type is suitable and
b)   the rollers are not sat on a bearer board

Fork lift truck safety

General safe driving rules

Although these trucks are mainly 'pedestrian operated', you're still the driver, and you can certainly do some damage or cause injury if you make a mistake.

So make sure you always follow these safety rules:

- Normal travel position is with the forks trailing. You should only use 'forks leading' when picking up and setting down a load

- Never ride on the truck unless it is fitted with a ride-on platform – and then only ride on the platform

- If riding on the flip-down platform, dismount to perform tight manoeuvres, negotiate slopes, pick up or deposit loads and load/unload vehicles

- Make sure there is sufficient standing space between the control handle and any obstacles behind you

- Most accidents on pedestrian operated trucks involve the truck coming into contact with the operator. So make sure you face in the direction of travel, standing to one side of the tiller arm with your arm fully outstretched to maximise the distance between yourself and the truck

MENTOR

Safe travel positions

The next three diagrams show how you should position yourself when using a pedestrian operated truck.

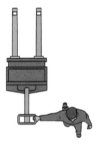

Forks trailing – moving in straight line

Walk to one side of the truck/tiller arm with your arm fully outstretched to maintain maximum separation between yourself and the truck.

Forks trailing – negotiating a turn

Walk on the outside of the turn with your arm fully outstretched to maintain maximum separation between yourself and the truck.

Forks leading – picking up/setting down

This method would normally only be used when picking up or setting down a load. Walk with both hands on the controls.

Principles of stability
(for pedestrian stacking trucks only)

Let's compare two examples to show how the size and position of the load affect the stability of a pedestrian stacking truck.

Example 1

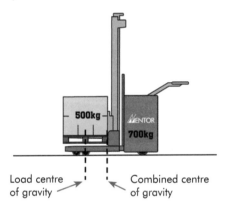

Load centre of gravity → ← Combined centre of gravity

In the above example, the load is being carried correctly – it is 'heeled' against the forks. To prevent the truck from tipping forwards, the combined centre of gravity of the truck and load must be inside the wheelbase of the truck.

> # Remember!
> All moving lift trucks, including pedestrian controlled trucks, are at their most stable when the load is carried as low and as far back as possible.

Example 2

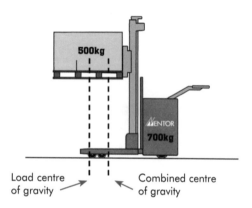

Load centre of gravity → ← Combined centre of gravity

In this example:

- Although the load is 'heeled' against the forks, the centre of gravity of the load is further forwards because the load is longer
- The load is also being carried higher

All this results in the combined centre of gravity of the truck and load coming dangerously close to moving outside of the wheelbase of the truck, at which point the truck could tip over.

Imagine the effect if the truck is moving, forks leading, and then you apply the brakes!

Pallet and load assessment

In addition to the normal pallet and load checks you would make before lifting a load, you need to make an extra check when using a pedestrian controlled truck:

Remember!

You must consider whether the truck you are using is suitable for the pallet type, as not all pallets can be lifted safely by all pedestrian truck types.

Let's look at two of the most common types of pallet.

Pallet 1. Two-way entry reversible

As this type of pallet is fully boarded on both sides,

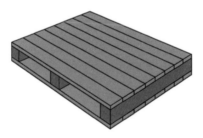

any type of truck which inserts anything apart from just the forks into the pallet **cannot** lift it.

So pallet movers, low level order pickers or support arm stackers are unsuitable for this type of pallet.

They can be lifted by:

- Pedestrian operated counterbalance or reach fork lift trucks, as they only insert the forks
- Straddle stackers, where the support legs are on the outside of the pallet

Pallet 2. Four-way entry non-reversible

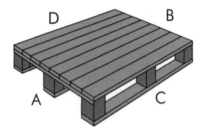

(The 800 x 1200 version is known as a 'Euro Pallet'.)

This type of pallet can be lifted by:

- Any truck type when entering it from sides A and B, as there are no boards below to foul the rollers (on pallet movers and low level order pickers) or the support legs (on support arm stackers)
- Pedestrian operated counterbalance or reach fork lift trucks and straddle stackers when entered from sides C or D

They **cannot** be lifted by entering from sides C or D by support arm stackers. However, they **can** be lifted by pallet movers and low level order pickers, providing the rollers on the legs are not sitting on one of the bearer boards.

Operating procedures

We'll now look at how to use pedestrian controlled stackers and powered pallet trucks.

Stacking with a pedestrian controlled stacker

Follow the procedures shown in the next six diagrams:

Step 1

- Approach the designated stacking location in the safe travel position with forks leading

- Turn through 90°, if required, to face the location, and stop with the front of the load 150mm from the racking or bulk stacking area and centrally positioned

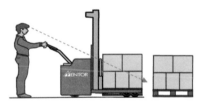

Step 2

- Ensure the tiller arm is in the fully up or fully down (brake applied) position
- Level the forks, if available
- Check above to ensure you have clear headroom before lifting
- Lift the load so the bottom of the pallet is 50-75mm above the racking or bulk stack

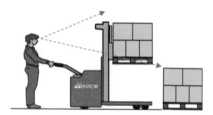

Step 3

- Look carefully all around you
- Position the tiller arm at the correct height to travel, and move forwards gently, under control, making any small steering corrections necessary to position the pallet correctly in its intended location
- Remember to position the pallet with a 50-75mm safety gap on each side of the load and, if stacking in racking, allow the pallet to overhang the front of the racking by 25mm-50mm. If bulk stacking, position the load exactly on top of the load beneath, keeping the stack perfectly upright and level

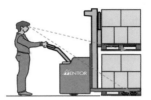

Step 4

- Position the tiller arm in the fully up or fully down (brake applied) position

- Lower the load smoothly, under control

- Position the forks at a height to clear the pallet without fouling on withdrawal

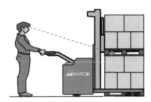

Step 5

- Look carefully all round you

- Position the tiller arm at the correct height to travel, and move away, looking in the direction of travel with occasional checks to ensure that the forks do not rub on the pallet on withdrawal

- If it looks like the forks may rub the pallet on withdrawal, stop and make the necessary adjustment, ensuring the tiller arm is in the fully up or fully down (brake applied) position before using the hydraulic controls

- Stop with the fork tips 150mm away from the load

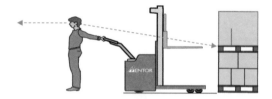

Step 6

- Position the tiller arm in the fully up or fully down (brake applied) position

- Lower the forks, under control, and place in the safe travel position

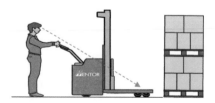

De-stacking with a pedestrian controlled stacker

Follow the procedure in the next six diagrams:

Step 1

■ Approach the designated de-stacking location in the safe travel position with forks leading

■ Turn through 90° turn, if required, to face the location, and stop with the fork tips 150mm from the racking or bulk stacking area and centrally positioned

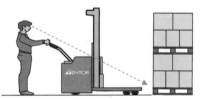

Step 2

■ Make sure the tiller arm is in the fully up or fully down (brake applied) position

■ Level the forks, if available

■ Check above to ensure you have clear headroom before lifting

■ Lift the forks to the correct height to enter the pallet cleanly

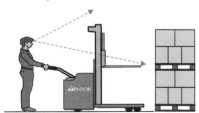

Step 3

- Look carefully all round you
- Position the tiller arm at the correct height to travel, and move forwards slowly, under control, making any slight steering adjustments needed until the fork heels gently kiss the pallet
- If it looks like the forks may rub the pallet on entry, stop and make the necessary adjustment, ensuring the tiller arm is in the fully up or fully down (brake applied) position before using the hydraulic controls

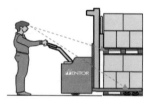

Step 4

- Position the tiller arm in the fully up or fully down (brake applied) position
- Check above to ensure you have clear headroom before lifting – pay particular attention to the backrest extension, if fitted
- Lift the pallet approx 50-75mm. If at this point the truck/forks/load dip forwards slightly due to a heavy load, apply a slight amount of back tilt, if available, to level the forks again so the load is level as you withdraw it

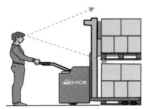

Step 5

- Look carefully all around you
- Position the tiller arm at the correct height to travel
- Move away, looking in the direction of travel with checks to ensure the pallet/load does not foul on the racking or adjacent loads on withdrawal. Make any slight steering adjustments as necessary to avoid this
- Stop with the load 150mm away from the racking

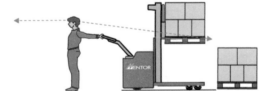

Step 6

- Position the tiller arm in the fully up or fully down (brake applied) position
- Lower the load, under control, and place in the safe travel position

Picking up with a powered pallet truck
Follow the procedure shown in the next five diagrams when picking up a pallet with a pedestrian controlled powered pallet truck:

Step 1

- Approach the pallet to be lifted in the safe travel position with forks leading
- Stop with the fork tips 150mm away from the load and centrally positioned

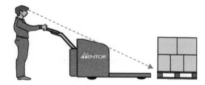

Step 2

- Position the tiller arm in the fully up or fully down (brake applied) position
- Position the forks at a height where they will enter the pallet cleanly

Step 3

- Look carefully all around you
- Position the tiller arm at the correct height to travel
- Move forwards slowly, under control, until the fork heels gently kiss the pallet

Step 4

■ Position the tiller arm in the fully up or fully down (brake applied) position

■ Lift the pallet clear enough of the ground to transport, taking ground conditions into account

Step 5

■ Look carefully all around you

■ Position the tiller arm at the correct height to travel

■ Move away in the safe travel position, looking in the direction of travel

Setting down with a powered pallet truck

Follow the procedure shown in the next five diagrams when setting down a pallet with a pedestrian controlled powered pallet truck:

Step 1

■ Move towards the pallet set down position in the safe travel position with forks leading

■ Stop with the front of the load in the correct position

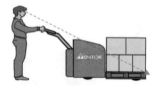

Step 2

■ Position the tiller arm in the fully up or fully down (brake applied) position

■ Lower the load to the ground under control

■ Position the forks at a height to clear the pallet without fouling on withdrawal

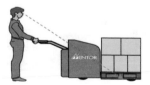

Step 3

■ Look carefully all round you

■ Position the tiller arm at the correct height to travel

- Move away smoothly, looking in the direction of travel with occasional checks to ensure the forks do not rub on the pallet on withdrawal
- Stop with the front of the forks 150mm from the pallet

Step 4

- Position the tiller arm in the fully up or fully down (brake applied) position
- Place forks in the safe travel position

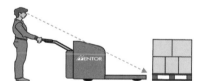

Step 5

- Position the tiller arm at the correct height to travel
- Move off under control, looking in the direction of travel

Summary

In this final section we've covered the various types of pedestrian operated trucks, looking at:

- Basic components
- General safe driving rules
- Principles of stability for pedestrian stacking trucks
- Pallet and load assessment
- Operating procedures

There's a truck load of information and guidance in this booklet – and we hope you've found it clear and useful!

But please don't just read the booklet and then put it away and forget about it.

Keep it handy and refer to it whenever you use a new type of fork lift truck or do a different task with your truck.

Practice the procedures until they become routine – this should be an uplifting experience!

Above all – always put safety first.